WORLD'S FAVORITE SERIES No. 19

WORLD'S FAVORITE ALBUM OF WEDDING SONGS

EDITED BY

ALBERT GAMSE

FOREWORD

We present here a comprehensive group of solos, ceremonial and recital music, processionals and recessionals associated with that most wonderful event — the wedding. These are arranged for medium voice solo, or piano. Chord symbols for accordion, guitar, organ etc. are included.

The piano accompaniments are of moderate grade and the vocal selections are presented in medium keys. Singable English translations have been provided for the magnificent arias that have found international favor at wedding ceremonies all over the world. Chord symbols have been added. The performance of music on piano, accordion, guitar, and organ, with the simple use of the symbol, has become increasingly popular in recent years.

We dedicate the collection to all weddings, and we hope this volume will be retained and treasured throughout the entire life of the newlyweds, long beyond the time they celebrate their Golden Wedding to the tune of "La Cinquantaine".

The Publisher

© Copyright 1962 by
ASHLEY PUBLICATIONS, INC.
39 West 60th Street, New York 23, N.Y.
International Copyright Secured   Made in U.S.A.

CONTENTS

	Page
A DREAM .... J. C. Bartlett and Charles B. Cory	37
ANDANTE CANTABILE (from Symphony No. 5) Peter Ilyich Tschaikowsky	50
ANDANTINO .... Edwin H. Lemare	34
ARIOSO .... Johann Sebastian Bach	31
AVE MARIA .... Bach-Gounod	46
AVE MARIA .... Franz Schubert	40
BARCAROLLE (from Tales of Hoffman) .... Jacques Offenbach	53
BECAUSE .... Edward Teschemacher & Guy d'Hardelot	22
BELIEVE ME IF ALL THOSE ENDEARING YOUNG CHARMS .... Thomas Moore	74
BELOVED, IT IS MORN .... Emily Hickey and Florence Aylward	150
BE THOU WITH ME .... Johann Sebastian Bach	131
BRIDAL CHORUS (from Lohengrin) .... Richard Wagner	4
CLAIR DE LUNE (de la Suite Bergamasque) .... Claude Debussy	56
DEVOTION (Widmung) .... Robert Schumann	144
DRINK TO ME ONLY WITH THINE EYES .... Ben Jonson & Wolfgang Amadeus Mozart	148
ENTREAT ME NOT TO LEAVE THEE (Song of Ruth) .... Charles Gounod	60
EVENING STAR (O Thou Sublime Sweet Evening Star) .... Richard Wagner	66
FIRST PIANO CONCERTO (Theme) .... Peter Ilyich Tschaikowsky	68
FOR YOU ALONE .... P. J. O'Reilly & Henry E. Geehl	70
GOLDEN WEDDING, THE (La Cinquantaine) .... Gabriel-Marie	158
HAVAH NAGILAH (Let Us Rejoice) .... Traditional	155
HOLD THOU MY HAND .... C. S. Briggs	26
I LOVE THEE (Ich Liebe Dich) .... Edvard Grieg	12
I LOVE YOU TRULY .... Carrie Jacobs-Bond	14
JESU, JOY OF MAN'S DESIRING .... Johann Sebastian Bach	140
JUNE (Barcarolle) .... Peter Ilyich Tschaikowsky	76

	Page
LARGO (from Xerxes) .... Georg Friedrich Handel	78
LIEBESTRAUM (Dream of Love) .... Franz Liszt	80
LOVE THEME (from Romeo and Juliet) .... Peter Ilyich Tschaikowsky	86
LOVE'S OLD SWEET SONG .... G. Clifton Bingham & J. L. Molloy	84
MEDITATION (from Thais) .... Jules Massenet	88
MELODY OF LOVE .... H. Engelmann	95
MY HEART AT THY SWEET VOICE (from Samson and Delilah) .... Kathleen Armour & Camille Saint-Saens	92
MY HEART EVER FAITHFUL .... Johann Sebastian Bach	136
MY WORLD .... Marguerite Sanders & Henry Geehl	96
NOCTURNE .... Frederic Chopin	105
O PERFECT LOVE .... Joseph Barnby	16
O PROMISE ME .... Reginald DeKoven	20
OUR WEDDING PRAYER .... George Geiger & Alma Hatton	100
PANIS ANGELICUS (O Lord of Mercy) .... Michel Whitehill & César Franck	102
PLAISIR d'AMOUR (The Joy of Love) .... Giovanni Martini	108
POSTLUDE .... Joseph Haydn	49
PRELUDE (Opus 28, #7) .... Frederic Chopin	127
PROCESSIONAL .... Georg Friedrich Handel	32
RECESSIONAL .... Henry Purcell	33
REVERIE .... Claude Debussy	110
ROMANCE .... Anton Rubinstein	114
ROSARY, THE .... Robert Cameron Rogers & Ethelbert Nevin	117
SERENADE .... Franz Schubert	112
STILL AS THE NIGHT .... Carl Bohm	120
SWEETEST STORY EVER TOLD, THE .... Robert M. Stults	124
TO A WILD ROSE .... Edward MacDowell	129
TRAUMEREI .... Robert Schumann	128
TRIUMPHAL MARCH .... Edvard Grieg	134
TRUMPET TUNE .... Henry Purcell	11
WEDDING MARCH (from A Midsummer Night's Dream) .... Felix Mendelssohn	6

GUEST LIST — Page 160

©Copyright 1962 by **ASHLEY PUBLICATIONS, INC.** • 39 West 60th Street, New York 23, N. Y.
International Copyright Secured   Made in U.S.A.   *All Rights Reserved Including Public Performance for Profit*

The Bride _____

The Groom _____

The Place _____

The Date _____ The Clergyman _____

Maid of Honor _____

Best Man _____

Bridesmaids: Ushers:

_____   _____

_____   _____

Singer _____

Instrumentalist _____

BRIDAL CHORUS
(FROM "LOHENGRIN")

RICHARD WAGNER

Allegro con Moto

© Copyright 1962 by Ashley Publications Inc.

WEDDING MARCH
(FROM "A MIDSUMMER NIGHT'S DREAM")

FELIX MENDELSSOHN

Allegro maestoso

© Copyright 1962 by Ashley Publications Inc.

TRUMPET TUNE

HENRY PURCELL

© Copyright 1962 by Ashley Publications Inc.

I LOVE THEE

EDVARD GRIEG

© Copyright 1962 by Ashley Publications Inc.

O PROMISE ME

REGINALD DeKOVEN, Op. 50

Moderato con espressione

O prom-ise me that some day you and I will
O prom-ise me that you will take my hand. The

take our love to-geth-er to some sky. Where we can be a-lone and faith re-
most un-worth-y in this lone-ly land. And let me sit be-side you. In your

new and find the hol-lows where those flow-ers grew.
eyes see - ing the vi - sion of our par - a - dise. Those

© Copyright 1962 by Ashley Publications Inc.

BECAUSE

Text by EDWARD TESCHEMACHER

Music by GUY d'HARDELOT

© Copyright 1962 by Ashley Publications Inc.

ARIOSO

JOHANN SEBASTIAN BACH

© Copyright 1962 by Ashley Publications Inc.

PROCESSIONAL

Andante (with dignity)

GEORG FRIEDRICH HANDEL

© Copyright 1962 by Ashley Publications Inc.

RECESSIONAL

Moderato (with dignity)

HENRY PURCELL

© Copyright 1962 by Ashley Publications Inc.

ANDANTINO

EDWIN H. LEMARE

Andantino molto sostenuto

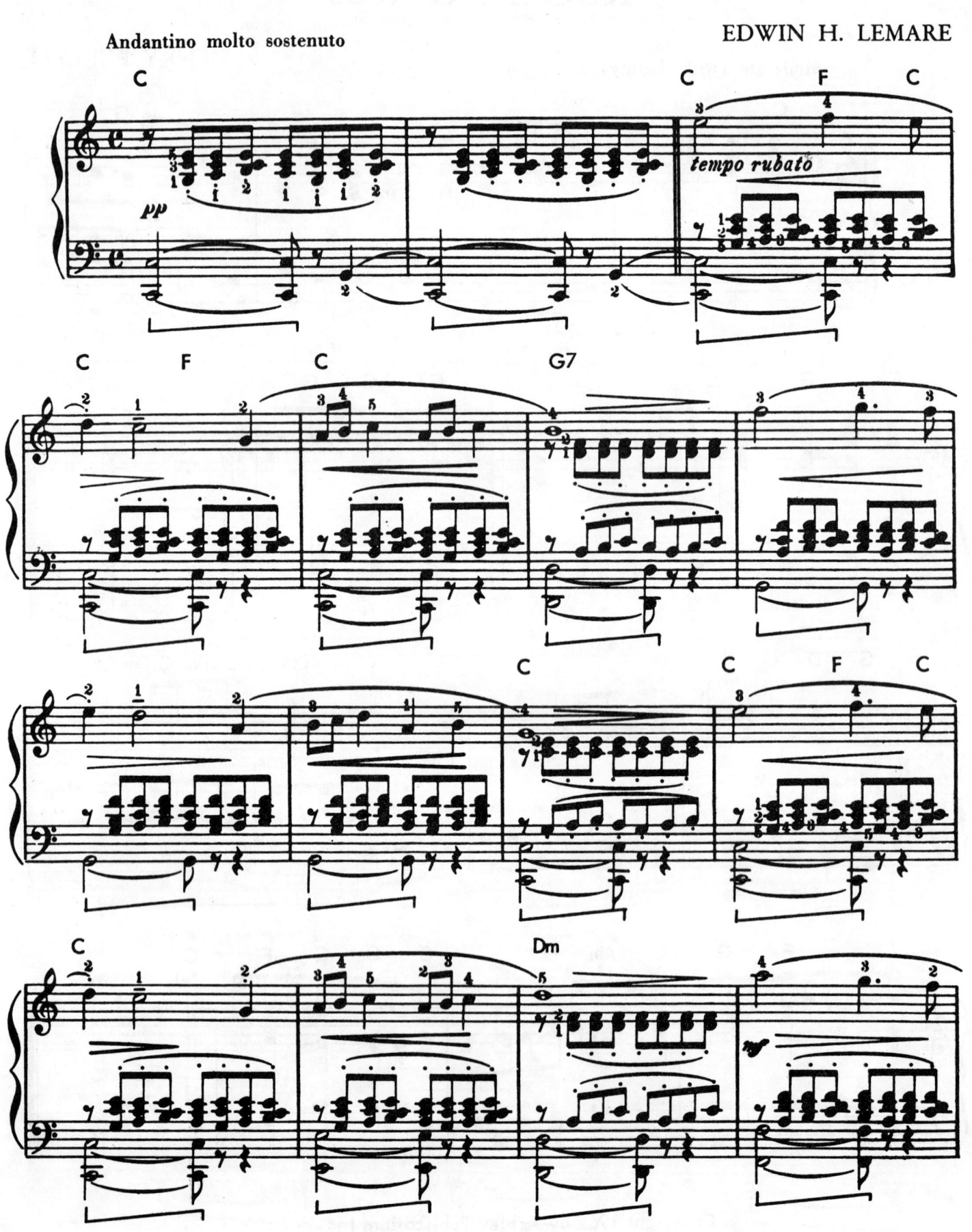

© Copyright 1962 by Ashley Publications Inc.

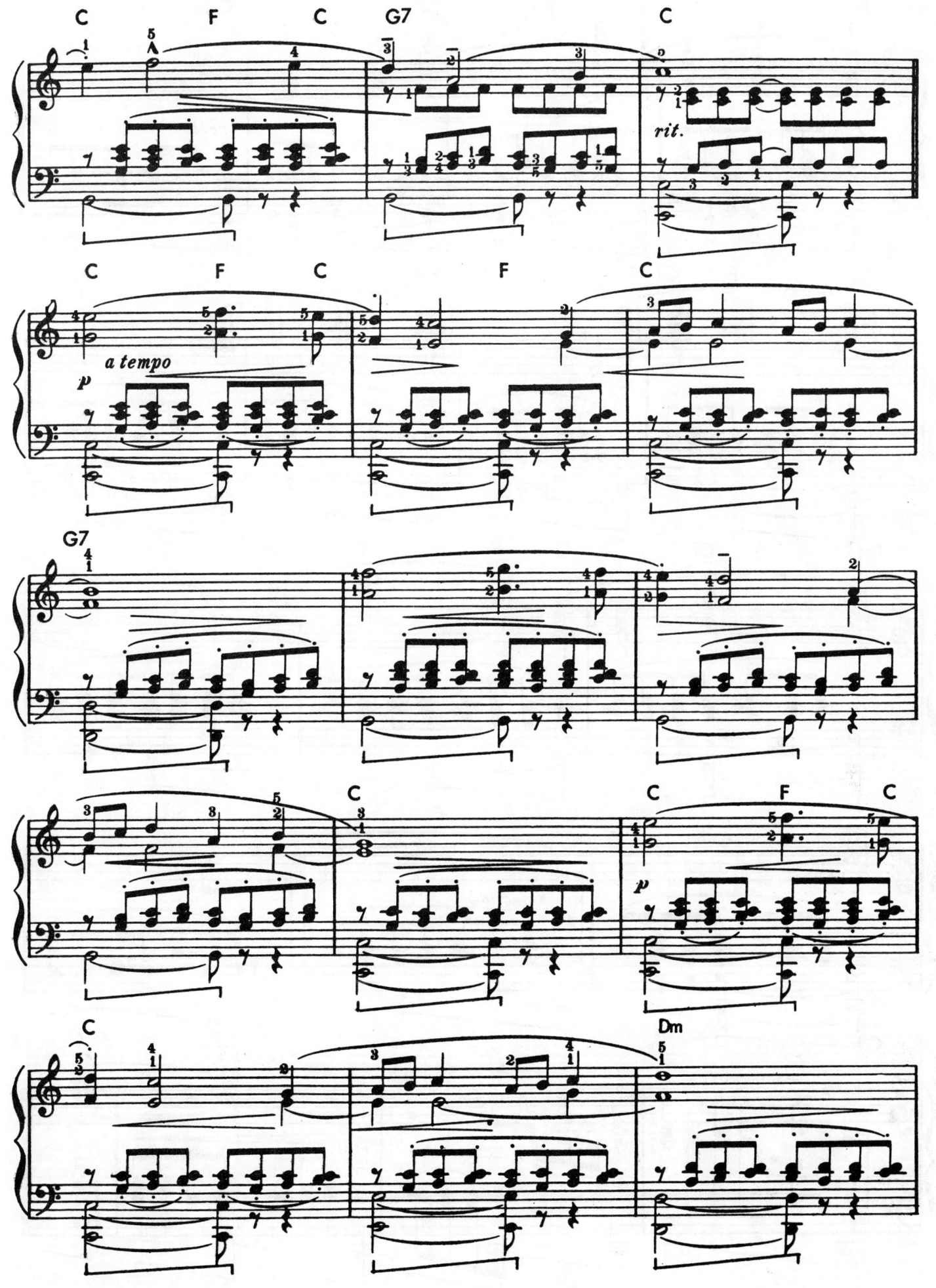

A DREAM

Text by CHARLES B. CORY

Music by J. C. BARTLETT

© Copyright 1962 by Ashley Publications Inc.

AVE MARIA

FRANZ SCHUBERT, Op. 52

© Copyright 1962 by Ashley Publications Inc.

Fm Fm6 Eb F7
fair. Bless this love, this heav-en-ly hour so
wild soll mein Ge - bet zu dir hin-
na, A - ve, A ve! Do - mi-
Eb Bb7 Eb Eb7 Ab
fair, Bless this hour so fair! Safe may we sleep beneath Thy care, And
we - hen. Wir schla - fen si-cher bis zum Mor-gen, ob
nus, Do-mi-nus te-cum. Be-ne-di - cta tu in mu-li-e-ri-bus, et
Eb7 Fm Eb C7 Bbm
guard this love we so tenderly share! O Maid - en, send your heavenly answer! O
Men - schen noch so grau-sam sind. O Jung - frau, sieh' der Jung-frau Sor-gen, o
be - ne-di - ctus, et be - ne-di-ctus fru-ctus ven-tris, ven-tris
fp
Abo Eb Eb7 Ab Fm6 Ab Eb7
Maid - en, hear this fervent pray'r. A - ve Ma - ri -
Mut - ter, hör' ein bit-tend Kind! A - ve Ma-ri -
tu - i, Je - sus. A - ve Ma-ri -
pp

Ab Ab7 Db Dbo Ab
a!
a!
a!
Ab Fm6 Ab Eb7 Fm Bbm Eb7
A - ve Ma-ri - a! O lis-ten to a
A - ve Ma-ri - a! Un be
A - ve Ma-ri - a! Ma - ter_ De -
Ab Ab+ Fm Fm6(+9) G7 Dbo
prayer! We pray, O Ma-ri-a, hear this pray - er! We need Thy blessing this hour so
fleckt! Wenn wir auf die-sen Fels hin - sin - ken zum Schlaf, und uns dein Schutz be-
i, O - ra pro no-bis pec-ca-to - ri-bus, O - ra, o - ra pro no -
Fm Fm6 Eb F7 Eb Bb7 Eb
fair. Bless this love, this heavenly hour so fair, Bless this hour so fair! Safe
deckt, wird weich der har-te Fels uns dün - - ken. Du
bis, O - ra, o - ra_ pro no - bis_ pec-ca-to - ri-bus, nunc,

43

Ab Fm6 Ab Eb7 Fm Bbm Eb7
mf
A - ve Ma-ri - a! O list-en to a
A - ve Ma-ri - a! Rei - ne
A - ve Ma-ri - a! gra - ti - a ple -
mf
Ab Ab+ Fm Fm6(+9) G7 Dbo
prayer! O give to this love eter - nal wis - dom, And keep it safe from harm and
Magd! Der Er - de und der Luft Dä-mo - nen, von dei - nes Au-ges Huld ver-
na, Ma-ri - a, gra - ti - a ple - na, Ma-ri - a, gra-ti-a ple-
Fm Fm6 Eb F7 Eb Bb7 Eb
woe, Make this love a love that will constantly grow, safe from harm and woe. O
jagt, sie kön - nen hier nicht bei uns woh - nen! Wir
na. A - ve, A - ve! Do-mi-nus, Do-mi-nus te-cum; Be-ne-
Eb7 Ab Eb7 Fm
Maid - en guard our love from harm, O Maid - en, guard our love from harm. O
woll'n uns still dem Schick-sal beu - gen, da uns dein heil'-ger Trost an-weht; du
di - cta tu in mu-li-e-ri-bus, et be - ne-di - ctus, et

45

Maid - en, send thy heav-en-ly an - swer, bless this love from your throne a-bove!
Jung - frau wol - te hold dich nei - gen dem Kind, das für den Va - ter fleht!
be - ne - di - ctus fru - ctus ven - tris, ven - tris tu - i, Je - sus.

A - ve Ma - ri - a!
A - ve Ma - ri - a!
A - ve Ma - ri - a!

AVE MARIA

Adapted by CHARLES GOUNOD
from BACH's "Well Tempered Clavier"
Text from St. Luke

Andante con moto

Lyrics:
Fa - - - ther Al - might - - - y, Lord, — — we a - dore — Thee, Bend - - ing be - fore Thee! Hear us, un - worth - y tho' we
A - - - ve Ma - ri - - - a, gra - - ti - a ple - na, Do - - mi nus- te cum, be - - ne - dic - ta

© Copyright 1962 by Ashley Publications Inc.

47

E♭m Ab♭m6 B♭7 E♭
mf
hear us! O hear us! While — we bow be-fore — Thee,
ri - a Ma-ri - a, o - ra Pro no - bis,
Fm7 B♭7 C°
Humb - ly we a - dore Thee, Hear — us O
no - bis pec-ca-to - ri bus, nunc — et in
molto cresc.
E♭ Fm7 B♭7
f
hear — us, and let — Thy - bless - ing rest on
ho - - - ra, in ho - - - ra mor - tis nos trae,
E♭ E♭7 A♭ B♭7 E♭
ppp
us! A - - - men!
A - - - men! A - - - men!
rall. e dim. poco a poco

POSTLUDE

JOSEPH HAYDN

ANDANTE CANTABILE

Andante cantabile con espressione

PETER ILYICH TSCHAIKOWSKY, Op. 64

Copyright 1962 by Ashley Publications Inc.

C7 Fm B♭7 E♭ Cm6 E♭ Cm6 B♭7
rall. e dim.
G Più mosso D7 G D7
mf
G Cm G C
mp
mf
Cm G C° G
mf
mp
C° Tacet E♭
p cresc. poco a poco rall. e dim.
p

Bb7 Eb Ab Bb7
Tempo primo
cresc.
Eb Bb7 Eb
decresc.
cresc.
Cm6 D7 Gm Bbm6 C7 Fm
a tempo
mf
rall.
Bb7 Eb Cm6 Eb Cm6 Bb7 Eb Bbm6
assai sostenuto
p
C7 Fm Bb7 Eb Cm6 Bb7 Eb Bb7 Eb
rall. e dim.
pp
smorzando

BARCAROLLE

Moderato

JACQUES OFFENBACH

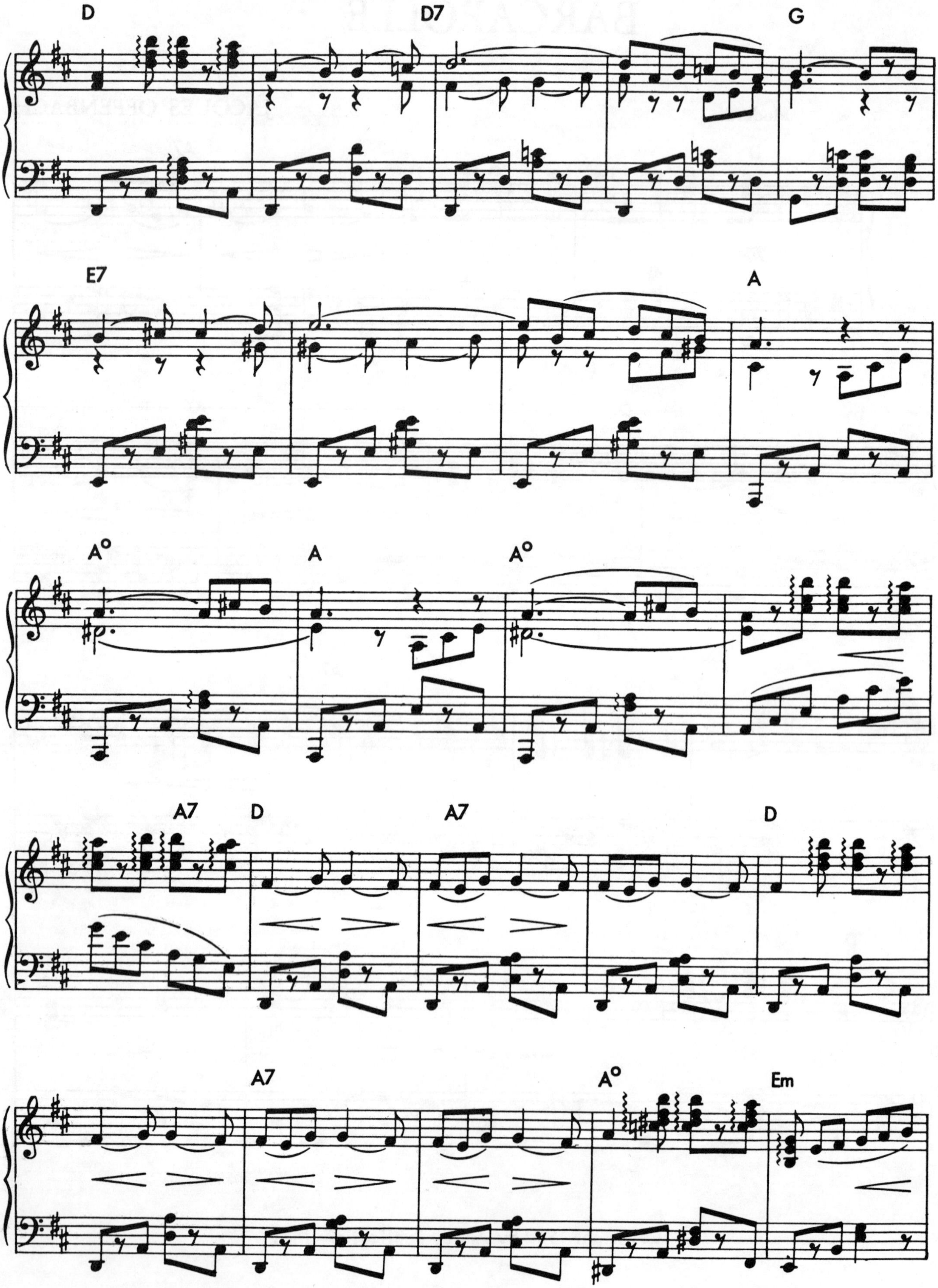
D
D7
G
E7
A
A°
A
A°
A7
D
A7
D
A7
A°
Em

55

CLAIR DE LUNE
(DE LA SUITE BERGAMASQUE)

Andante molto espressione

CLAUDE DEBUSSY

© Copyright 1962 by Ashley Publications Inc.

57

Cm Ab Cm Ab
più cresc.
Bb Fm Cm F7 Bb7
f
dim.
G7 F G7 F G7
pp
F G7 Dm F G7 F G7 F Fm
C E G F G F G
Tempo I
ppp

59

ENTREAT ME NOT TO LEAVE THEE
(SONG OF RUTH)

CHARLES GOUNOD

And Ruth said: En-treat me not to leave thee, En-treat me not to leave thee, or

© Copyright 1962 by Ashley Publications Inc.

to re-turn from fol-low-ing af-ter thee, for whith-er thou go-est, I will go, and where thou lodg-est I will lodge, whith-er thou go-est I — will go, and where thou lodg-est — I will lodge. — Where thou lodg-est, where thou lodg-est, I will lodge. — Thy

un poco meno presto, ma pochissimo.

peo-ple shall be my peo-ple, and thy God my God, thy peo-ple shall be my peo-ple, and thy God my God, Thy peo-ple shall be my peo-ple, and thy God my God.

Where thou di-est, will I die, and there will I be bur-ied — The Lord do so to me, and more al-so, if aught but death part thee and me, if aught but death part thee and me. Thy

peo-ple shall be my peo-ple, and thy God, my God, Thy peo-ple shall be my peo-ple, and thy God, my God, Thy peo-ple shall be my peo-ple, and thy God, _____ thy God, my God.

EVENING STAR
(O THOU SUBLIME SWEET EVENING STAR)

Andante

RICHARD WAGNER

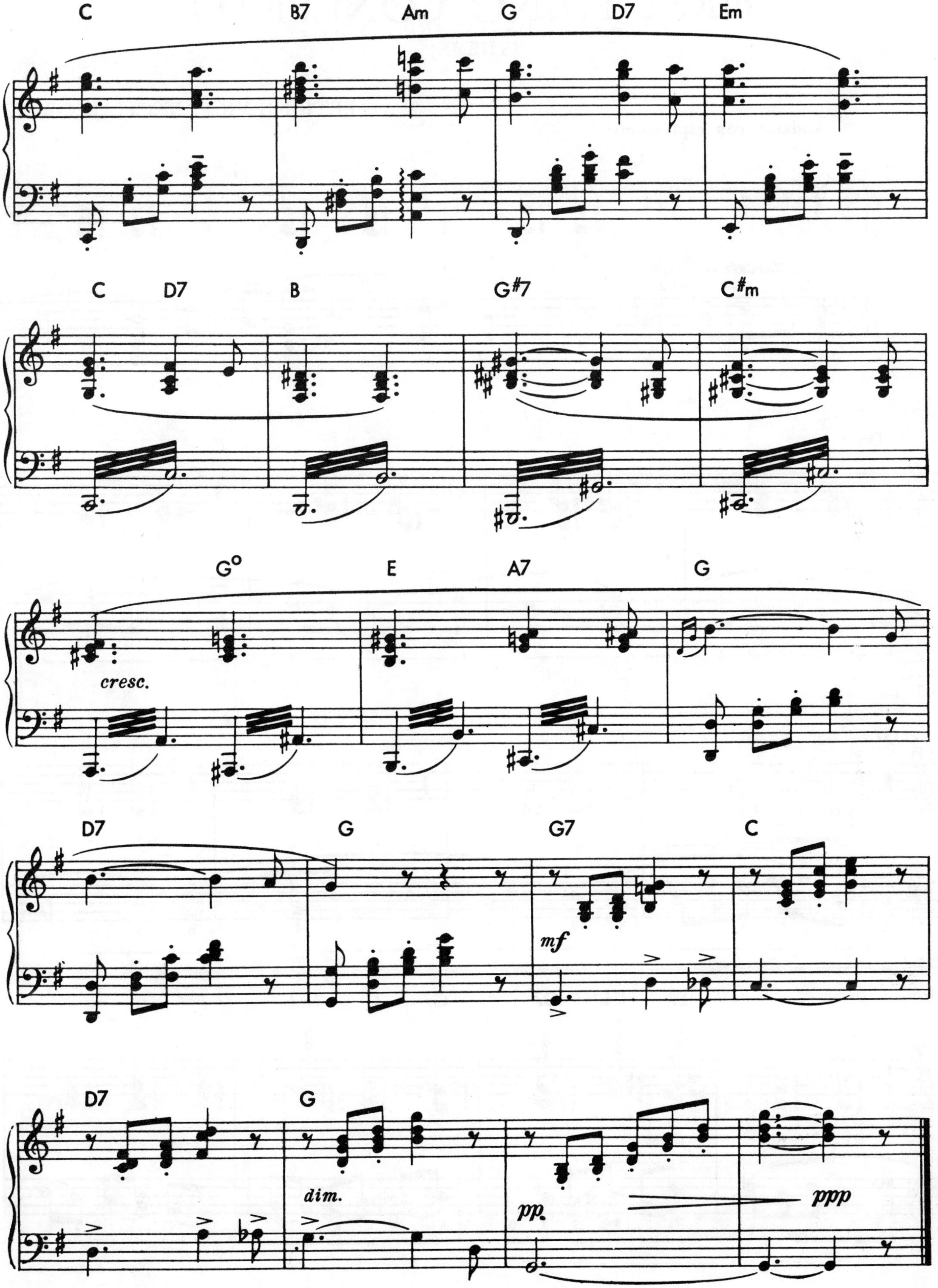
C B7 Am G D7 Em
C D7 B G#7 C#m
G° E A7 G
cresc.
D7 G G7 C
mf
D7 G
dim.
pp.
ppp

ND

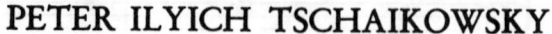

D7 G7 C
tempo
rall. e dim.
più f
F
C G7
C G7 C G7 C
molto cresc.
f
C Dm G7 E A7 D7
Maestoso
f
G7 C D7 C D D7 D C
rall. e dim.
pp

FOR YOU ALONE

Text by P. J. O'REILLY

Music by HENRY GEEHL

Andantino

Take thou this rose, this lit-tle ten-der rose, The rar-est flow'r in all God's gard-en fair, And

© Copyright 1962 by Ashley Publications Inc.

let it be while yet its crim - son glows

An em - blem of the love ———— I proud - ly, proud - ly bear.

Take thou this heart, the heart that loves thee well, — And let it flame be-fore thy shrine, my own. — Take thou my heart, for oh, your dear eyes tell —

73

BELIEVE ME IF ALL THOSE ENDEARING YOUNG CHARMS

Text by THOMAS MOORE

TRADITIONAL MELODY

Be - lieve me, if all those en - dear - ing young charms, Which I gaze on so fond - ly to - day —— Were to change by to - mor - row and fleet in my arms, Like fai - ry gifts, fad - ing a -

It - is not while beau - ty and youth are thine own, And thy cheeks un - pro - faned by a tear, —— That the fer - vor and faith of a soul can be known, To which time will but make thee more

© Copyright 1962 by Ashley Publications Inc.

75

JUNE
(BARCAROLLE)

PETER ILYICH TSCHAIKOWSKY, Op. 37 No. 6

Andante espressivo

77

LARGO
(FROM "XERXES")

GEORG FRIEDRICH HANDEL

G C D7 G D C G
3
C D7 G D7 G C D7 G
D7 G6 D7 B B7 Em Am B7 Em C
f
p
D7 G D C G D7 G D7 G
f
C G C6 D7 G D7 G
rit.
ff

LIEBESTRAUM
(DREAM OF LOVE)

FRANZ LISZT

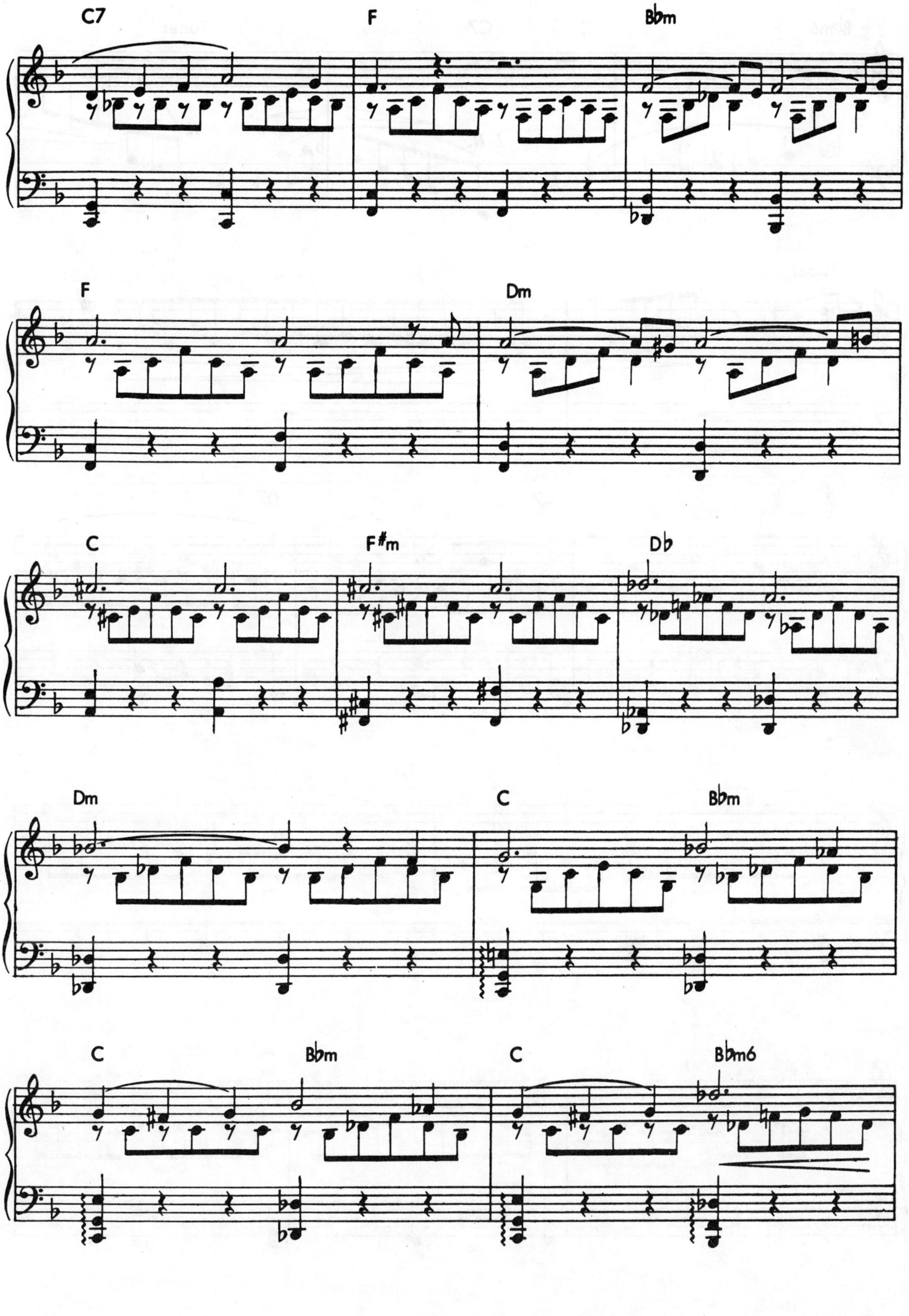
C7
F
B♭m
F
Dm
C
F♯m
D♭
Dm
C
B♭m
C
B♭m
C
B♭m6

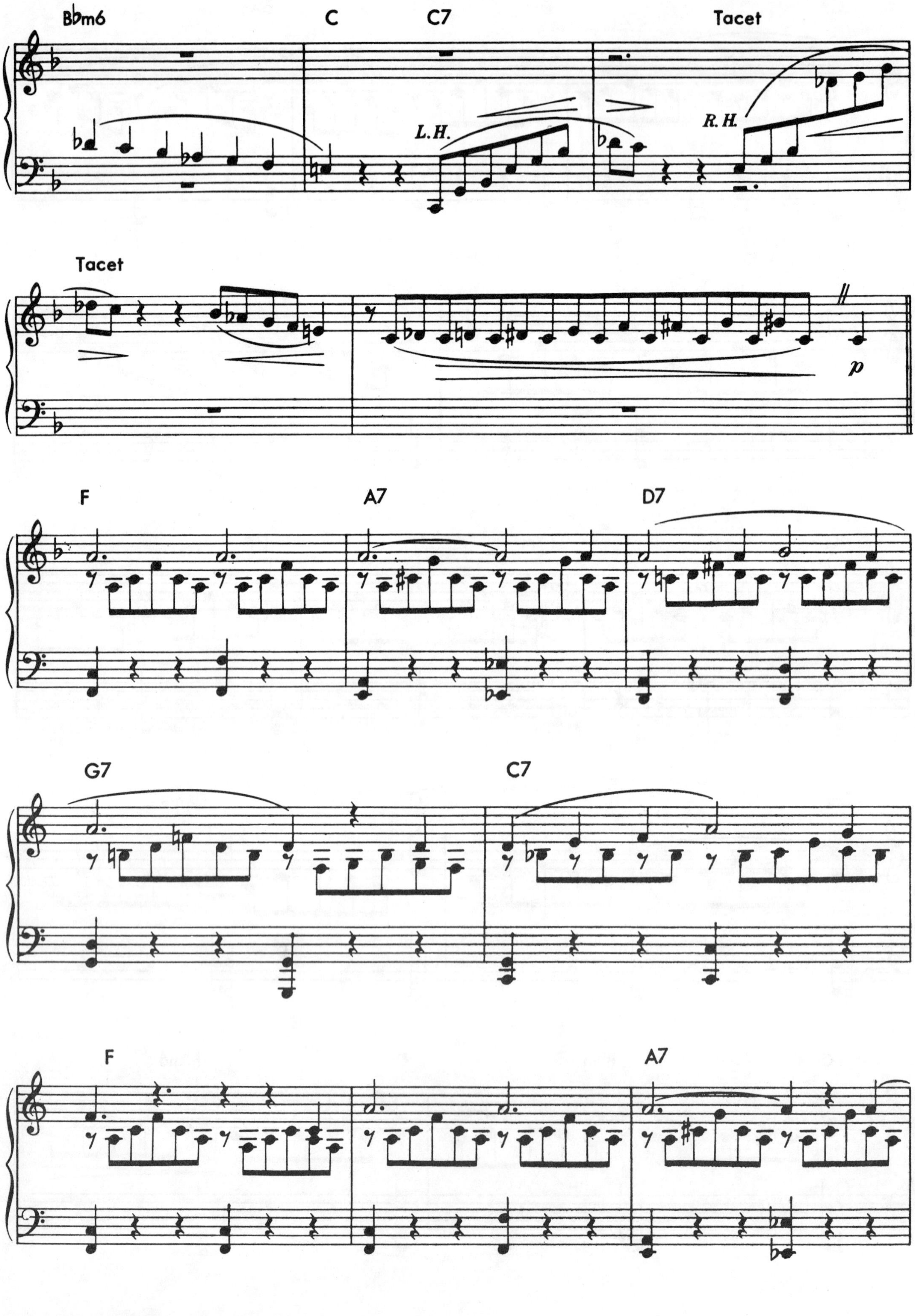
B♭m6
C
C7
L.H.
Tacet
R.H.
Tacet
p
F
A7
D7
G7
C7
F
A7

83

LOVE'S OLD SWEET SONG

Text by G. CLIFTON BINGHAM

Music by J. L. MOLLOY

Andantino con moto

1. Once in the dear, dead days beyond recall, When on the world the mist be-gan to fall, Out of the dreams that rose in hap-py throng, Low to our hearts love sang an old sweet song. And in the dusk, where fell the fire-light gleam, Soft-ly it wove itself in-to our dream.

2. E-ven to-day we hear love's song of yore, Deep in our hearts it dwells for-ev-er more, Foot-steps may falt-er, wea-ry grow the way, Still we can hear it at the close of day. So till the end, when life's dim shadows fall, Love will be found the sweetest song of all.

© Copyright 1962 by Ashley Publications Inc.

85

Just a song at twilight, When the lights are low, And the flick-'ring shadows — Softly come and go. — Tho' the heart be weary, Sad the day and long, Still to us at twilight, Comes love's old song, Comes love's old sweet song.

LOVE THEME
(FROM "ROMEO AND JULIET")

Andante cantabile

PETER ILYICH TSCHAIKOWSKY

87

MEDITATION
(FROM "THAIS")

JULES MASSENET

A7
dol.
Cresc.
Em7
p rall
A7
D
a Tempo
Dim
C
mf
F#7
Em
più f
A7
Poco a poco
G
Bm
Am
C7
dol.
f
p
Ped.
F
Cresc.
B♭m
Fm
f
B♭m
Fm
più f
G°
B♭m
G°
Fm

A7
E°
A7
E°
A7
sff
sff
sf
Très expressif
cédez un peu.
Tacet
p
rall
D
pp
G
Em
A
G
A7
B♭m
D
p
f
pp
Ped.
* 2 Ped.
C
Cresc.

91

MY HEART AT THY SWEET VOICE
(FROM "SAMSON AND DELILAH")

Text by KATHLEEN ARMOUR

CAMILLE SAINT-SAENS

Lyrics:
Just like the blush-ing rose, My true love blooms for you, dear, Mu-sic sweet your mer-ry laugh-ter, Whis-per to me a-gain, Tell me you love me tru-ly, That thru all e-ter-ni-ty — once

© Copyright 1962 by Ashley Publications Inc.

G7 E F7 E G7
more re-peat to me the vows I would hear, Once more re-peat to
E Fm6 B♭6
mf cresc.
me—, Tell it o - ver a-gain, Tell it o-ver a-gain.
8va
fz
C D7
Tell me that you love me with a love that's ev-er
mp
G7 C
mp
true. Sweet - est sto - ry ev-er
mp

told — but ev-er new. My heart at thy sweet voice, Ev-er it will re-joice, Hold me! Your arms en-fold me, O let me hear you say a-gain, I love you! Al - ways, al - ways, Al-ways, dear-est one, I'll love but you.

MELODY OF LOVE

Moderato con espressione

H. ENGELMANN, Op. 600

Copyright 1962 by Ashley Publications Inc.

MY WORLD

Text by MARGUERITE SANDERS

Music by HENRY GEEHL

Lento con espressione

God knew my need, and brought me to your feet,

God knew my want, and led me to your side,

© Copyright 1962 by Ashley Publications Inc.

God knew a joy to make my life com-plete, And let me there a-bide. God knew a dream with-in my in-most heart, God knew a hope that made my love di-vine, God heard a prayer in si-lent hours a-part, And made you whol-ly mine. And so for-ev-er thro' all years that roll,

99

And for the bless-ed beau-ty of His dower, I praise the great Re-deem-er from my soul, And love you more, and love you more each hour!

OUR WEDDING PRAYER

GEORGE GEIGER
ALMA HATTON

Lento con espressione

Oh Mary, Mother of our Saviour, _____ please bless us on our wedding
may we learn from tribulation _____ that sunshine always follows
Our Father give thy benediction, _____ please bless us on our wedding
may we learn from tribulation _____ that sunshine always follows

day, As hand in hand we journey on thru life, please
rain, And may our faith in God's great goodness grow thru
day, And as we journey hand in hand thru life, please
rain, And may our faith in Thy great goodness grow thru

walk with us along the way. Help us to bear in mind our
life's sweet joy and thru life's pain. We ask Your blessings now as
walk with us along the way. Help us to bear in mind our
life's sweet joy and thru life's pain. We ask Your blessings now as

© Copyright 1962 by Ashley Publications Inc.

blessings, please strengthen us thru ev'ry trial. Oh,
children, as children, guide us on our way. Dear
blessings, please strengthen us thru ev'ry trial. Oh,
children, as children, guide us on our way. Dear

Mary, Mother of our Saviour, we ask Your blessings on this
Mary, Mother of our Saviour, we thank You for Your love this
Father hear our suplication, we ask Your blessings on this
Father hear our suplication, we thank You for Your love this

day, And as we kneel before God's altar — Pray that our
day, And as we kneel before God's altar — Pray that our
day, And as we take our vows before Thee — Grant that our
day, And as we take our vows before Thee — Grant that our

love like Yours will last always. And
love like Yours will last always.
love like Yours will last always. And
love like Yours will last always.

PANIS ANGELICUS
(O LORD OF MERCY)

Music by CESAR FRANCK

O Lord of mer-cy, O Lord of jus-tice, Thine own and hum-ble ser-vants seek to find re-demp-tion with in-fin-ite wis-dom.

© Copyright 1962 by Ashley Publications Inc.

Thou dost look on us, Sa-viour, Sa-viour, Thou art mi-rac-u-lous, Sa-viour, Sa-viour, We would Thy ser-vants be. Sing-ing our praise to Thee, Thee our hearts do flee, Glo-rious Thy name shall be until e-ter-ni-ty. E'en in the si-lent night, Thy glo-ry shin-ing bright, Pro-claims to mor-tals Thy ev-er glo-rious might Fath-er of men To Thee we bring our song of praise.

NOCTURNE

FREDERIC CHOPIN, Op. 9 No. 2

Fm C Dm Gm C7 F F7 Bb
f a tempo
molto rit.
fz p
a tempo
Dm Gm G7 Fm Cm F D7 Gm G°
poco rit.
a tempo
F7 Bb F C7 Eb Ebm
p
pp rit.
Bb Fm C Dm Gm C7 F F7
f a tempo
molto rit.
Bb Dm Gm G7 Fm Cm
fz p
a tempo
poco rit.
a tempo

F7 D7 Gm G° F7 B♭ E♭m
B♭ E♭m B♭ F7 B♭ C
poco rubato
dolcissimo
F B♭ E♭m B♭ E♭m
rit.
a tempo
con forza
B♭ C7 D7 Gm C7 F7
stretto
B♭

PLAISIR d'AMOUR
(THE JOY OF LOVE)

Text by ALBERT GAMSE

GIOVANNI MARTINI

The joy of love ——— Is ours forever to share. ——— The joy of love is a treasure beyond compare. ——— As I stand proudly be-

© Copyright 1962 by Ashley Publications Inc.

109

REVERIE

CLAUDE DEBUSSY

111

SERENADE

FRANZ SCHUBERT, Op. 90 No. 11

Gm D A7 D G
1.
mf
pp
D A7 D A7
1.
2.
C9 A7 F# Bm Em
f>p
Bm G D A7 D
p
f
Dm Em7 A7 D Gm
pp
D A7 D
dim.

ROMANCE

ANTON RUBINSTEIN, Op. 44 No. 1

Moderato con moto

© Copyright 1962 by Ashley Publications Inc.

B♭
F7
D°
Cm
G7
Cm
G7
Cm
E♭m
F7
B♭
F7
D°
Cm
G7
Cm
F7
B♭7
E♭
A♭m6
p
B♭7
E♭
A♭
B♭7
E♭
B♭7
cres.
E♭
C°
Fm6
C

Ebm6
Bb
Ebm
G°
Bb7
rit.
Eb
a tempo.
Abm6
Bb7
E b
f
5
Abm6
Bb7
Eb7
Ab
G7
Cm
cres.
Abm6
Bb7
Eb
Abm6
f
f
p
Eb
8-

THE ROSARY

Text by ROBERT CAMERON ROGERS

Music by ETHELBERT NEVIN

Lento (intimo)

The hours I spent with thee, dear heart, Are as a string of pearls to me, I count them o-ver ev-'ry one a-part, My ro-sa-ry, my ro-sa-ry!

Comme un ro-sai-re sont pour moi Les heu-res qui nous u-nis-saient; Tou-jours je les comp-te pen-sant à toi, Beau-coup trop vite el-les pas-saient!

Oft denk' mit Weh-mut ich zu-rück Der hol-den Stun-den, reich an Glück, Die, strah-lend in der jun-gen Lie-be Glanz, Den Per-len gleich am Ro-sen-kranz

© Copyright 1962 by Ashley Publications Inc.

Each hour a pearl, each pearl a pray'r, To still a heart in absence wrung, I tell each bead unto the end, And there a cross is hung! O memories that bless and

Une prière à chaque grain Pour calmer mon coeur aux abois, J'arrive ainsi jusqu'à la fin, Mais là pend une croix! O doux moments si pleins d'é-

Wie sie, so reiht der Stunden Zahl, Ein lichter Kranz, sich jedes- mal Zur Kette von Gebeten fromm— Bis ich zum Kreuze komm! Im Geist entschwund'ner Selig-

Dm7 G7 C G#7 Dm7 G7
burn! O bar-ren gain and bit - ter loss!
moi, A vous tou-jours, je dois pen - ser,
keit Küss' ich sie all', in stum - mem Leid,
patetico
C7 F
mf sempre cresc.
I kiss each bead and strive at last to learn To kiss the
J'em - bras - se cha - que grain jus - qu'à la croix, Tâ - chant d'ap -
Bis end - lich mir der Schmerz der letz - ten Stund' Drängt, O Ge -
mf sempre cresc.
f
Am6 D7 C G7 C
f poco accel. ff Largo pp
cross, sweet - heart! To kiss the cross!
prendre en - fin à l'em - bras - ser.
lieb - - - - te(r), das Kreuz zum Mund.
poco accel.
f ff pp

STILL AS THE NIGHT

Text by GEORGE COOPER

Music by CARL BOHM

Still as the night, Deep as the sea, Should be thy love, my own!

Still wie die Nacht, tief wie das Meer, soll dei-ne Lie-be sein!

© Copyright 1962 by Ashley Publications Inc.

Bb Bb+ D7 Gm Bb7 Eb Gm
p poco a poco cresc.
Still as the night, And
Still wie die Nacht und
p poco a poco cresc.
Cm Ebm F7 C° F7 Bb F7 Bb
f
deep as the sea, Should be thy
tief wie das Meer soll dei - ne
f
Bb Eb Bb C7
love, thy love for me a - lone!
Lie - be, dei - ne Lie - be sein,
Bb F F7 Bb
pp
poco rit.
Should be thy love, my own!
soll dei - ne Lie - be sein!
pp
poco rit.
pp a tempo

When thou dost love, As doth my heart,
Wenn du mich liebst so wie ich dich,

Time ne'er our lives shall part!
will ich dein ei - gen sein.

Glow - ing like steel, And
Heiss wie der Stahl und

PRELUDE

FREDERIC CHOPIN, Op. 28 No. 7

TRAUMEREI

ROBERT SCHUMANN

TO A WILD ROSE

Moderato (tenderly)

EDWARD MacDOWELL

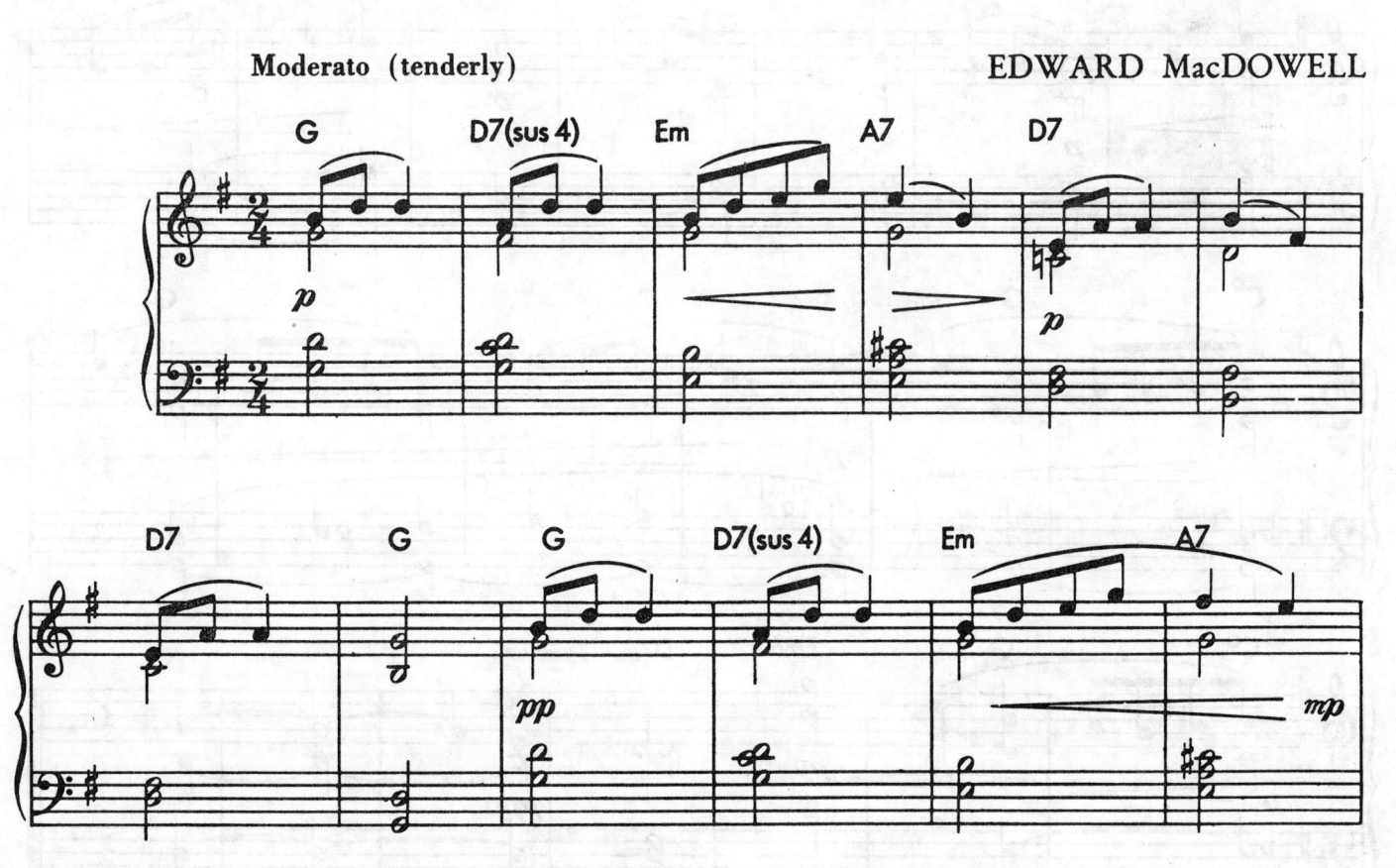

© Copyright 1962 by Ashley Publications Inc.

G Bm D7 G D7 C
p
pp
C° G Gmaj7 G° Gmaj7 G°
inercase
still inercase
D7 Am6 G D7(sus 4) G
f
rit.
p
A7 D7 Bm D7 G D7(G) C
p
C° G G° C C° G
mp
C° G Em6 D7 G
p
pp
ppp

BE THOU WITH ME

Versified Translation by ALBERT GAMSE

JOHANN SEBASTIAN BACH

Bist du bei mir, geh' ich mit Freu-den zum Ster-ben und zu mei-ner Ruh', zum Ster-ben und zu mei-ner Ruh'. Bist du bei mir, geh' ich mit Freu-den

Be Thou With Me, Then go I glad-ly, to face what-ev-er des-ti-ny may hold. To face the days as they un-fold. Be Thou With Me, Then go I glad-ly,

© Copyright 1962 by Ashley Publications Inc.

132

zum Ster-ben und zu mei-ner Ruh', zum ___ Ster-ben und zu mei-ner Ruh'.
To face the days as they unfold, To face the days as they unfold.

Ach wie ver-gnügt wär' so mein En - de: Es drück-ten
Glad would I be, if thou were with me, To close my

dei-ne schö-nen Hän-de mir ___ die ge-treu-en Au-gen zu.
eye-lids with thy hands, To close my eye-lids with thy hands.

133

TRIUMPHAL MARCH

EDVARD GRIEG

135

MY HEART EVER FAITHFUL

(MEIN GLAUBIGES HERZE)

JOHANN SEBASTIAN BACH

G D7 G D7 G D7 G C6
Je - sus ist nah!
Je - sus is near!
mf
G D7 G G7 C6 C7 F
Weg Jam - mer, weg Kla - gen, weg Jam - mer, weg Kla - gen, ich
A - way with com-plain-ing, a - way with com-plain-ing, Faith
dim.
p
Dm E7 Am E Am E
will euch nur sa - gen, mein Je - sus ist da; weg Jam-mer, weg Kla-gen, ich
ev - er main-tain-ing, My Je - sus is here. A - way with com-plaining, Faith
poco cresc.
dim.
p
F E7 C6 Dm Am E7 Am
will euch nur sa - gen, mein Je - sus ist da, mein Je - sus ist da;
ev - er main-tain-ing, My Je - sus is here, my Je - sus is here.
mf
(Tacet)
weg
A-
cresc.

C6 C° D Gm C7 F G7
Jam - mer, weg Kla - gen, weg Jam - mer, weg Kla - gen, ich will — euch nur sa - gen, mein
way with com-plain-ing, a - way with com-plain-ing, Faith ev - er main-tain - ing, My
p
C7 F G7 C G7 C G7
Je - sus ist da! Mein gläu - bi-ges Her - ze, froh - lo - cke, sing', scher-ze,
Je - sus is here! My heart, ev-er faith-ful, Sing prais - es, be joy-ful,
mf
C F6 C G7 C C G7
mein gläu - bi-ges Her - ze, froh -
My heart, ev-er faith-ful, Sing
dim.
p
C G7 C F6 C G7 C
lo - cke, sing', scher-ze, froh - lo - cke, sing scher - ze, dein Je - sus ist da, froh -
prais - es, be joy - ful, sing prais - es, be joy - ful, Thy Je - sus is here, Sing

F D7 G E7 Am F G7
lo-cke, sing', scherze, froh - lo - - - cke, sing', scher - -
prais-es be joy-ful, sing prais - es, be joy - -
dim.
C F6 C G7 C G7 C G7
- ze, mein gläu - bi-ges Her-ze, froh - lo - cke, sing', scher-ze, froh-
- ful, My heart, ev-er faith-ful, Sing prais - es, be joy-ful, sing
p
C F6 C G7
lo - cke, sing', scher - ze, dein Je - sus ist da!
prais - es, be joy - ful, Thy Je - sus is here!
mf
C G7 C F6 C G7 C
cresc.
f

JESU, JOY OF MAN'S DESIRING

JOHANN SEBASTIAN BACH

141

Em Am G Am G D7
G D Em D7 C D G D Em Em7 Am D7 A7 Em D7
G A7 D7 Am G Am Dm7 C G7 C G7 Em
Am F E7 Dm Em C F Fmaj7 Dm E7 F7 D Em E7 Am G
cresc.
f
C C6 D C7 Dm G C C7 F Em Dm G
dim

C D G D G D7 C D G D G C G C D7 G Am Em
D A D G6 D7 G D7 G C D G D G Bm Em
cresc.
f
Am D7 A7 D7 G G7 C D7 G
Am D7 G Am D G D Em Am D7 G Am G
pp
D7 G C D7 Am G D Em G Em Am A7 Em D G
molto ritard
D. S.
Fine.

DEVOTION
(WIDMUNG)

Versified German Text by ALBERT GAMSE

ROBERT SCHUMANN

Allegro animato

Du meine Seele, du mein Herz, du meine Wonn', o du mein Schmerz, du meine Welt, in der ich lebe, mein Himmel

Thou art my soul, thou art my heart. My life, my joy, my pain, thou art. Thou art the world where I reside, My heav'n's

© Copyright 1962 by Ashley Publications Inc.

Bb F7 Bb+ Gm C7 G°
du, da - rein ich schwe - be; o du mein Grab, in das hin -
here, dear, at your side — Thou art the earth where woes are
F7 Bbm F C7 F
ab ich e - - wig mei - nen Kum - - mer gab!
laid a - way, Ah love I know thy worth!
rit.
Db Gb Db Gb Ab7
Du bist die Ruh', du bist der
Thou art the life a - bove the
p
Db Fm Db Abm6 Bb7 Ebm Abm7 Db
Frie - den, du bist vom Him - mel
mort - al, sent here to me through

Gb Eb7 Db Ab Ab7 Db Ab7
mir ___ be - schie - den. Dass du mich liebst, macht mich mir
Heav - en's port - al. To hold thy hand, to share thy
Gb Db Db7 Gb Db7 Eb
werth, ___ dein Blick hat mich vor mir ver - klärt, ___ du hebst mich
kiss, what great - er prize have I than this? My hopes, my
rit.
C7 C6 F Bb
lie - bend ü - ber mich, mein gu - ter Geist, mein bess'res
dreams, the best in me, Are brought to light when I'm with
p
rit.
C7 F C F
Ich! Du mei-ne See - le, du mein Herz, du mei-ne
thee. Thou art my soul, thou art my heart, My life, my
a tempo
f

Wonn', o du mein Schmerz, du mei-ne Welt, in der ich le-be, mein Him-mel du, da-rein ich schwe-be, mein gu-ter Geist, mein bess'-res Ich!

joy, my pain, thou art, Thou art the world where I re-side, my heav-en's here, dear, at your side, my bet-ter self, my life, my all!

DRINK TO ME ONLY WITH THINE EYES

Text by BEN JONSON
Music by WOLFGANG AMADEUS MOZART

Moderato

Drink to me on-ly with thine eyes, and I will pledge with mine. Or give a kiss with-

I sent thee late a ro-sy wreath, not so much hon-'ring thee, As giv-ing it a

© Copyright 1962 by Ashley Publications Inc.

C G7 C7 Dm A Fm6 C Dm7 C G7 C
in — the cup — and I'll — not ask for wine. —
hope — that there — it would not with - ered be. —
C G7 C7 F C
cresc.
— The thirst that from the soul doth rise, doth ask a
— But thou there - on didst on - ly breathe, and send'st it
pp
cresc.
C Dm C D7 G7 C G° Dm F7
drink di - vine, — But might I of Jove's
back to me, — Since when it grows and
mf
C G7 C7 Dm A Dm7 C Dm7 C dim. G7 C
pp
nec - tar sip —, I would not change for thine. —
smells, I swear, not of it - self but thee. —
rall. e dim.
pp

BELOVED, IT IS MORN

Text by EMILY HICKEY

Music by FLORENCE AYLWARD

© Copyright 1962 by Ashley Publications Inc.

A red-der ber-ry on the thorn, A deep-er yel-low on the corn, For this good day new-born.

Pray, sweet, for me, That I may be Faith-ful to God, to God and thee. Be-lov-ed, it is day! And lov-ers work as chil-dren play, With heart and brain un-tired al-way, Dear love, look up, look up and pray, —— Look up and pray. ——

153

Fm Fm6 C Fm C Am6 F° Gm G° Gm G° Am7
clear and white. God keep thee in His sight,
cresc.
F6 G7 C Am F6 G7 C F6 C F Fm6 C C7 Am C7
God keep thee in His sight. Pray, sweet, for me,
p
F Fm6 C C7 F6 C7 F6 C G7 Am D7 Fm7 C Am
That I may be Faith - ful, faith - ful to
p
F6 G7 C7 F6 C7 F F° C
God and thee.

HAVAH NAGILAH
(LET US REJOICE)

Arranged by ALBERT GAMSE

Con vigor (tempo di hora)

Ha - vah ___ na - gi - lah, Ha - vah ___ na - gi - lah,
Ha - vah ___ na - gi - lah, Ha - vah ___ na - gi - lah,

Ha - vah ___ na - gi - lah, vay - nis - m'chayh,
Ha - vah ___ na - gi - lah, Sing! Let us re - joice!

Ha - vah ___ na - gi - lah, Ha - vah ___ na - gi - lah,
Ha - vah ___ na - gi - lah, Ha - vah ___ na - gi - lah,

© Copyright 1962 by Ashley Publications Inc.

156

157

Ha - vah n' - ra - ne - nah, vay - nis - m' - chayh.
Wake with a hap-py heart, Sing! Let us re - joice!

Moderato

U - ru, U - ru a - chim, U - ru a - chim b' lev sa - me - ach,

mf (gradually increase tempo)

U - ru a - chim, b' - lev sa - me - ach, U - ru a - chim, b' - lev sa - me - ach, U - ru a - chim, b' - lev sa - me - ach, U - ru a - chim! b' - lev sa - me - ach.

D.S. al Fine

THE GOLDEN WEDDING
(LA CINQUANTAINE)

GABRIEL-MARIE

Allegretto

159

Guest's Signatures